Horse Properties
A Management Guide

Jane Myers and Equiculture I

GW00683336

ISBN: 978-0-9945722-0-2

Email: stuart@equiculture.com.au

Disclaimer

The authors and publisher shall have neither liability nor responsibility to any person or entity with respect to any loss or damage caused or alleged to be caused directly or indirectly by the information contained in this book. While the book is as accurate as the authors can make it, there may be errors, omissions and inaccuracies.

About this book

This book is a guide to the *sustainable* management of a horse property. It covers the **horse characteristics** that you need to understand in order to manage horses and the land that they live on. It also covers a **fresh approach** to land management that encompasses horse welfare, good environmental management and time/budget saving strategies. This method is something we call **The Equicentral System** and we have been teaching horse owners about this system for several years now, in fact horse owners around the world have implemented this horse management system to great effect. Do yourself, your horses, and the land that they live on a favour and read this book!

Thank you for buying this book and please consider either leaving a review or contacting us with feedback, stuart@equiculture.com.au.

About the authors

Jane Myers MSc (Equine Science) is the author of several professional books about horses including the best selling book Managing Horses on Small Properties (published by CSIRO). Jane is particularly interested in sustainable horsekeeping practices and issues, such as low stress horse management that also delivers environmental benefits. Jane has lived and breathed horses from a young age and considers herself to be very fortunate in that she has been able to spend her life riding, training and studying these amazing animals.

Stuart Myers (BSc) has a background in human behaviour and has been a horse husband for more years than he cares to remember.

Jane and Stuart present workshops to horse owners in Australia, the USA and the UK about sustainable horse and horse property management as part of their business, Equiculture.

See the Equiculture website:
www.equiculture.com.au
where you will find lots of great information about horsekeeping. Jane and Stuart also have another website that supports their Horse Rider's Mechanic series of workbooks. This website is
www.horseridersmechanic.com

Contents

Photo credits: All photos and diagrams by Jane Myers and Stuart Myers unless otherwise accredited. Any errors and omissions please let us know.

Introduction

Healthy Land = Healthy Pasture = Healthy Horses.

There are *numerous* benefits to managing the land that horses live on as well as possible, these are just some of them:

- **Lower feed bills** due to more home grown feed (pasture) being available for a longer period of the year.
- **Less or no skin/hoof problems** due to there being less or no mud.
- **Less or no issues associated with dust** including dust related issues with people living nearby.
- **More provision for habitat for wildlife** such as insect eating birds etc. which leads to fewer pest insects such as irritating flies.
- **Cleaner and more abundant water**.
- **An increased land value/better public perception**.
- **Reduction in time spent on chores and a reduction in expense**.
- **Improved health and happiness** for the horses *and* people that live on the land.

Good land management is a win win for all!

This book is intended as a **guide** only and complements our **Healthy Land, Healthy Pasture, Healthy Horses** talk. For more in depth information on any of the subjects in *this* book see **The Equicentral System series** of books listed at the end.

Pasture grown for horses also protects the soil and helps to keep the waterways clean by filtering out nutrients.

Horse characteristics and behaviours

In order to manage the land that horses live on well it is essential to learn about certain normal/natural *and* abnormal/unnatural horse characteristics and behaviours. Naturally-living (wild/feral) horses have a very different 'lifestyle' to domestic horses.

The main differences between the lifestyle of naturally-living horses compared to domestic-living horses are:

- **Naturally-living horses** are highly social animals and therefore they live in herds/bands and have rich and varied social lives. **Domestic-living horses** are often prevented from interacting with other horses which can cause high levels of stress in an animal that would never live alone by choice.
- **Naturally-living horses** are able to make group *and* individual decisions about where they want to be throughout the day. **Domestic-living horses** usually have no control over where they are at any point in their lives.
- **Naturally-living horses** are on the alert for many hours a day, although this behaviour is shared with other members of the herd. **Domestic-living horses** are not usually in danger from predators etc. but they do not know this. They feel safer in a herd because they can then share 'looking out for danger' between herd members.
- **Naturally-living horses** eat a very high fibre/low sugar/low starch/low protein diet and graze or forage for many hours a day. **Domestic-living horses** often have a diet that is inappropriately high in energy and too low in fibrous roughage.

Domestic-living horses are often prevented from interacting with other horses which can cause high levels of stress in an animal that would never live alone by choice.

- **Naturally-living horses** go through cycles of gaining and losing weight throughout the various seasons of the year. **Domestic-living horses** are usually 'micro managed' so that they maintain the same weight throughout the year, rather than losing a little over winter.
- **Naturally-living horses** travel large distances on a daily basis, from feed to water and back again in what is known as the '**home-range**' (a large area that contains the resources that they need i.e. food/water/shade/shelter). **Domestic living horses** often receive too little exercise and, instead of having to find their own food and water, it is given to them 'on a plate'.
- **Naturally-living horses** cope with a variety of climates and changing seasons ranging from very cold and wet, to very hot and dry and everything in between. **Domestic-living horses** rarely have to deal with temperature extremes. Modern rugs and stables result in many domestic horses never experiencing the need to use energy to keep warm.
- **Naturally-living horses** tend to have a shorter life span than domestic horses. **Domestic-living horses** generally live much longer. In fact, it is not uncommon for them to reach their thirties and forties.
- **Naturally-living horses** *usually* show very little aggression; particularly with regard to physical contact which could result in injury and *decrease* their chance of survival through predation or starvation. **Domestic-living horses** may be forced to defend themselves and/or their food. For example, we tend to initiate aggression when we feed concentrates to horses that are kept together.
- **Naturally-living horses** are able to control parasitic worms by avoiding eating near their own dung. **Domestic-living horses** may be forced to graze badly managed 'horse sick' pasture that contains high levels of parasitic worms.

Naturally-living horses are highly social animals.

Daily 'time-budgets'

Many species of animal have been studied in their natural habitat to find about their daily 'time budget'. An understanding of how horses naturally use their time helps with their grazing management and therefore land management.

The time - budget of horses includes a lot of grazing.

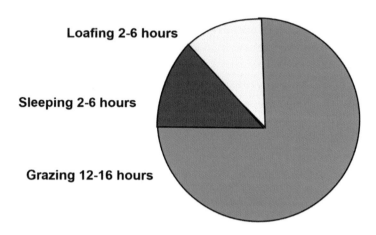

Loafing 2-6 hours

Sleeping 2-6 hours

Grazing 12-16 hours

Grazing

Horses have one of the **longest daily grazing periods** of all the plant eating herbivores. Horses graze in what are termed 'bouts' which typically last between 1.5 to 3 hours. Horses *usually* carry out their grazing bouts throughout the day and night with 'bouts' of sleeping and 'loafing' (being social) in between.

*Horses have one of the **longest daily grazing periods** of all the plant eating herbivores.*

The total daily grazing time of a horse depends on the **quality** of pasture available. On 'better' quality (higher calorie) pasture a horse will spend less total time grazing (approximately 12-14 hours a day) and more time sleeping and loafing. In harsher conditions (such as drought or a very cold/wet winter) when the pasture is 'poor' quality (lower in calories) and more fibrous, a horse will spend up to 20 hours a day grazing/browsing if necessary. In this case social behaviour becomes a low priority and they do little more than sleep, search for food and eat, in order to survive.

Sleeping

Adult horses sleep/snooze for about four hours a day, approximately two hours are spent lying down and two standing up. A horse must lay flat out in order to get enough rapid eye movement (REM) sleep. They can snooze, but not sleep deeply, while standing. This total time of about four hours is split into bouts of around 15 minutes at a time throughout the day and night. In very wet weather horses will often wait until the sun comes out to lay down rather than lay down in the rain.

A total of approximately two hours a day are spent lying down - flat out.

In a group of horses, one horse usually stays standing when the others are asleep on the ground.

Loafing

Loafing describes all the other things that horses do with their day, such as mutual grooming, playing and simply standing around together, being social. These behaviours are **very important** for a horse's well being and generally take up a total of about four hours a day.

'You scratch my back and I'll scratch yours'.

Standing around together is of top priority to horses, they will often **disregard other comforts** in order to be able to stand near other horses. This is seen when horses are kept separately in 'private paddocks' where they will **ignore** shade/shelter in order to stand next to each other on either side of the fence.

When horses are kept separately in 'private paddocks' they will often ignore shade/shelter in order to stand next to each other on either side of the fence.

The grazing behaviour of horses

Horses are herbivores; they eat plants and lots of them. This natural food source for horses is **low in calories** and takes a long time to collect, chew and digest.

Here are some interesting facts about horses and their grazing behaviour:

- Their physiology is different to that of many other grazing herbivores in that they are *not* ruminants (like cattle and sheep). Horses eat relatively *more* food but digest it *less* efficiently than most ruminants. Because of this fact, horses spend *more time* grazing than cattle and sheep and they *ferment* their food in the hind-gut while grazing. Ruminants spend a lot of their time ruminating (regurgitating and re-chewing their food) *as well* as grazing.
- Put another way, horses **eat more** but invest **less time** on each mouthful of food, ruminants **eat less** but invest **more time** on each mouthful of food.
- This strategy means that horses are generally more successful than ruminants in very **tough** conditions when the feed source becomes more fibrous or lower in nutritional quality. A horse's digestive system has evolved to allow them to survive in very harsh conditions.

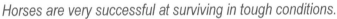

Horses are very successful at surviving in tough conditions.

The importance of fibre to horses

Acid **continuously builds up in the stomach of a horse**. The acid in the stomach **is usually buffered** by the saliva that a horse swallows while chewing fibrous material. An important point here is that saliva flows *in response* to food in the mouth (not at the thought of food as it does with say humans and dogs). If a horse does not have access to enough fibre and therefore is not chewing and swallowing enough saliva, this acid reaches critical levels in the stomach and causes gastric ulcers.

Not getting enough fibre is also one reason why domestic horses will sometimes eat poisonous plants, strip the bark from trees etc. - they are desperate for fibre.

Food selection in horses

Grass is a horse's **main staple** although they will eat other plants, bushes and trees including berries and fruit sometimes. The naturally-living horse's diet is usually much more varied than that of a domestic horse. Their diet is not balanced daily, but it becomes a balanced diet throughout the year as different plants are available to be eaten throughout the various seasons.

Selective grazing habits of horses

Horses are highly selective grazers, their prehensile (highly flexible) top lip allows them to be **very selective** in what they eat and what they leave. They also have two sets of incisors which meet together and are very sharp. This means they can bite plants down to ground level. Horses, if left on a pasture for too long, will continuously select plants that they like and graze them to the ground, leaving the rest to grow long and rank. The long, rank areas are also where they drop their dung (see the section **The 'dunging behaviour' of domestic horses**).

Their prehensile (highly flexible) top lip allows them to sort what they want from what they do not want as they graze.

Horses have no concept of 'leaving some for another day' or any other grazing management strategy that would result in **more grass in the future**. If grass is available horses will eat it, even if they make themselves incredibly fat in the process or if they completely eat out their favoured species. Instead they are driven by their **innate** need to eat whenever possible so that they can build up fat reserves to get them through the next harsh period such as winter or drought.

Horses have no concept of 'leaving some for another day' or any other grazing management strategies that would result in more grass in the future.

Walking while grazing

While a horse is grazing, they are also walking because the plants are stationary and the horse has to keep moving in order to graze them. Whilst grazing they will cover approximately 12 miles to 24 km each day! This slow, steady movement is vital for horse health.

If a horse is grazing they are also walking. Grazing creates movement and therefore exercise.

The pastured behaviour of domestic horses

Domestic horses have certain behaviours that come about *because* they live in captivity. Again, you need to understand these behaviours - and how you can govern or reduce them - so that you can manage the land that you have available to you and your horses as well as possible.

The 'standing around behaviour' of domestic horses

When not grazing, horses will stand around (loaf), sometimes for hours at a time, for various reasons. Horses often have a favourite 'hanging out' area such as somewhere that is shady/sheltered, near resources such as water, a high flat area or, most often, this spot is near the gateway.

Factors that increase 'standing around behaviour':

- **Being turned out on bare (overgrazed) 'pasture'.** As already mentioned, grazing and walking are *linked* behaviours so if there is no pasture to eat horses will simply stand around (once they have run off any excess energy).
- **Being turned out on pasture that is a monoculture** (only contains a limited number of plant species). Horses soon discover if there are only one or two types of plant to eat. This causes them to **reduce** their time spent seeking out variety and instead overgraze the area nearest to where they can see supplementary feed approaching (usually near the gateway).
- **Being fed supplementary feed.** A horse will stand around (usually at a gateway) and wait, long before feed time (even if there is plenty of pasture available). The *anticipation* of concentrate feed causes horses to **reduce** their grazing bout time and increase their time spent standing.

Horses that are being fed supplementary feed will stand around (usually at a gateway) even if there is plenty of pasture available.

The problem with gateways

So you can see that gateways in particular are often very **high use** areas on a horse property, and the land just beyond the gateway is often the most heavily *grazed* area of a paddock. For the various reasons outlined before, horses can spend *a lot* of their time standing in this area.

This hanging around behaviour adds to the already heavy use of the gateway area, causing more soil compaction, dust, mud and weeds. More dung is also dropped in this area, adding to the muddy 'soup' when the weather is wet. This means that a horse may be standing for hours in filthy muddy conditions and it is therefore not surprising that horses in this situation are prone to certain fungal/bacterial skin and hoof conditions such as mud fever/greasy heel/thrush.

In the naturally-living situation, horses will *never stand for hours* in mud, instead, they will take themselves to a higher, drier area.

Gateways and just beyond them are often the most degraded area in a paddock.

One of the main reasons that horses stand in gateways is, as already mentioned, because this is where concentrate feed is delivered, or where a horse is collected from and taken *to* concentrate feed.

Please note: we are not for a moment suggesting that providing additional feed for your horse/s is a bad thing. We are simply keen to describe how supplementing the diet is *linked with land management problems*. In most cases in a domestic situation we *have* to provide supplementary feed to horses, at least at certain times of the year. It is important to understand though that the very first time we provide supplementary feed for a horse, we encourage these behaviours. Once you understand what is happening and why horses do the things they do you may be able to make changes that improve the situation - more on this later.

The 'tracking behaviour' of domestic horses

Horses create 'tracks' in areas that they *frequently travel*. These pathways are usually between areas such as a shelter and the gate, a water point and the gate and so on. The soil in these pathways soon becomes compacted and bare. Soil erosion occurs in these pathways because water is able to move faster in these areas than the surrounding areas. This speeds up the process so that these pathways become ever deeper and ever more eroded.

A common sight - horses create 'tracks' in areas that they frequently travel.

The 'fence walking' behaviour of domestic horses

'Fence walking' is a stereotypical (stressed) behaviour. It causes the same soil degradation problems as 'tracking behaviour'. Horses 'fence walk' because they are trying to get to somewhere or something (usually another horse) and the fence is preventing them from doing so.

'Fence walking' creates the same problems for the land as 'tracking behaviour'.

The 'dunging behaviour' of domestic horses

A typical poorly managed horse paddock has areas of long rank grass and weeds, called 'roughs', and areas that are overgrazed, called 'lawns'. This occurs because horses generally deposit their dung in certain areas of the paddock (unlike other grazing animals that tend to drop it more randomly around the paddock). When a paddock has these marked areas it is also called 'horse sick'.

If left unattended the 'roughs' tend to get larger over time because horses tend to drop their dung on the outside edges of them. Horses generally avoid grazing near their own dung because of the parasitic 'worms' that they can pick up in that area (all grazing animals avoid eating near their own species' dung for this reason). Therefore the roughs become high in nutrients and the lawns become nutrient deficient. The lawns tend to be overgrazed and will eventually become bare and compacted as the horses graze the pasture right to the ground.

'Horse-sick' pasture.

This diagram show the typical land degradation problems that occur on a horse property due to the various issues outlined in this section.

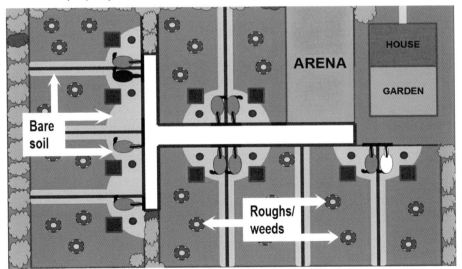

Horses and land degradation

The easily visible signs of land degradation are 'horse sick' pasture, bare soil, soil erosion, dust, mud, weed infestations and dead or dying trees.

Horses *will* cause damage to land when they are allowed to *overgraze* land (which includes spending too much time standing around on it). Overgrazing in particular occurs when there are too many horses for the amount of land available. This damage can be alleviated by careful management (see the section **Pasture/grazing management**).

Allowing horses to overgraze and degrade the land *now* sets up problems *for the future.* *Some* of the main effects of overgrazing are:

- **Reduced horse health** - dust and mud cause respiratory and skin conditions.
- **Reduced soil quality** - Unhealthy soil is generally compacted, has a mineral imbalance and is lacking in micro-organisms.
- **Less and less *healthy* pasture over time** - more stressed grasses (and therefore more dangerous to graze).
- **Less biodiversity** - the grasses that do survive tend to be short varieties that are low in fibre/high in sugar.
- **More opportunities** for weeds/poisonous plants to become established.
- **Increased soil loss** - top soil is being lost at an alarming rate in many countries around the world. For example the UK has lost 80% of its topsoil since 1850 and is still losing it at an average rate of 1-3 cm per year!
- **Reduced water quality** - any soil, manure or other pollutants that enter a waterway has an impact on the quality of the water further along the water system.
- **Reduced land value** - degraded land is worth less.

Bare soil is just one sign of land degradation. Unfortunately it is a common sight on a horse property.

- **Increased horsekeeping costs** - you will need to spend more money on 'bought-in' feed.
- **Reduced wildlife habitat** - this leads to other problems such as large numbers of pest insects due to a shortage of insectivorous birds or insectivorous bats to eat them. In turn this means that more pesticides need to be used.

Soil loss- top soil is being lost at an alarming rate in many countries around the world. Without top soil healthy pasture cannot grow.

Remember: horses cause wear and tear to land by grazing but also by the other behaviours that they carry out i.e. by their 'standing around behaviour' and 'tracking behaviour'.

Remember: fences and gates *prevent* horses from being able to move themselves to where they want/need to be, so often they have no choice but to stand for hours at a gate or under a tree.

Good land management involves removing this 'pressure' whenever possible. A horse does not mind where they carry out these behaviours, they simple require a good surface, shade/shelter and water. Therefore they may as well carry these behaviours out in an area that is *designed* to cope with this pressure so that the pasture can have *more time* to rest and recuperate.

Whenever horses are not grazing, they should carry out all other behaviours in an area that is created for that purpose and, if possible, they should be able to take themselves to that area. See the section The Equicentral System for information about how you can encourage horses to *voluntarily* eliminate this pressure on the land.

Bare/compacted soil and erosion

A typical order of occurrence is too much grazing pressure (overgrazing, combined with hoof pressure), which leads to bare soil or mud/dust, leading to soil compaction and, ultimately, soil erosion.

Due to the fact that water *cannot* penetrate compacted soil any rain runs off the land and takes any loose topsoil and manure with it. When the weather is dry the wind then removes yet more topsoil. So, it can be seen that the situation becomes a *downward spiral of events*.

Compacted soil, even after heavy rain, is unable to absorb water.

If it is necessary to reduce the grazing pressure on your pasture, and therefore bare soil, compaction etc., the best way to do this is to adopt the attitude that if the horses are not grazing they should not be in the paddock.

As well as the potential damage that horses can cause to the land if they are not managed correctly, a horse owner needs to be aware of the problems of **too much water** and **not enough water** arriving on the land.

Too much water

Mud occurs when there is too much grazing or standing pressure on land that is wet. It may be because the soil is a type, i.e. clay, that retains too much moisture and/or it may be that the underlying soil, which should allow drainage, has become compacted through mismanagement. If you have waterlogged soil, it will need careful management if it is not to become worse.

Remember: when horses spend too much time on land in this condition, they churn up the soil and create a 'soup' of water and manure (mud).

Grazing wet land will lead to muddy conditions and 'pugging'.

In addition to making the task of caring for horses harder work, mud has many disadvantages for horse health:

- It creates a breeding ground for insects such as mosquitoes and midges.
- It can cause injuries - horses (and people) can slip or fall.
- Feeding horses on muddy ground leads to soil/sand ingestion.
- Bacteria and fungi proliferate in muddy conditions; these cause skin and hoof conditions in horses.

In a naturally-living situation horses can usually take themselves to higher, drier ground when they wish. When domestic horses are fastened in a paddock, they cannot do so, so it is up to you to make sure horses do not *have* to stand around in wet conditions.

Horses do not voluntarily stand around in muddy conditions.

Not enough water

Dry conditions bring their own problems:

- Most grass plants are less able than most weeds to access underground water due to having generally shorter roots.
- The hot weather that is usually coupled with dry conditions means that the plants become increasingly dehydrated, stop growing and will shatter and eventually die if grazing animals are allowed to overgraze them at this time.
- If pasture is overgrazed and good plants die out then this gives weeds the opportunity to grow when the dry period breaks.
- Plants that horses may usually ignore (such as poisonous plants) are often all that is left to graze when the good plants have been grazed out.
- When the soil is dry, the ground is also hard and dusty. Hard ground jars the legs of horses and dust causes eye and respiratory problems (for horses *and* people).

Your primary aim during dry conditions/drought should be damage control:

- Aim to remove grazing pressure when the plants are about 5cm (2ins) in height or higher in order to minimise land degradation; this will help to protect the soil from harsh, dry, hot weather.

Remember: if there is no grazing available, you will need to *remove* the horses from the area to protect the remaining plants and soil, otherwise you will further compact and damage the soil, making recovery much more difficult. A 'sacrifice area' can also be used (see the section 'Sacrifice areas').

*Once the drought is over, resist the temptation to turn horses out until the pasture has **fully recovered**, and start with just a few hours at a time.*

Weeds

What is a weed? A plant that is in the wrong place at the wrong time would be one way of defining a weed. The term weed covers a huge range of plants and what is classed as a weed to one group of people may be a beneficial herb or useful plant to another.

Weeds tend to be strong competitors, moving in when conditions favour them, especially when the soil is bare or in poor condition. They range from plants which are simply unwanted, to noxious plants that cause huge problems for people, animals and the environment. Some weeds are highly invasive of both native and agricultural land. These types of weeds often have particularly vigorous characteristics which is why they are so important in terms of controlling them. Some of these weeds may be also poisonous to horses.

What is classed as a weed to one group of people may be a beneficial herb or useful plant to another.

Certain characteristics are common amongst weeds and help to ensure their survival. Weeds *tend* to possess one or more of the following characteristics:

- Abundant seed production (large numbers of seeds are shed).
- Rapid establishment (the seeds can become established quickly and easily).
- Long seed dormancy (seeds remain viable for a long time).
- Adaptation for spread (seeds are easily dispersed).
- Ability to easily occupy sites disturbed by human activities (bare soil).
- High NSC (sugars, starches) content to enable them to grow quickly.

However, *some* weeds can actually have certain beneficial qualities:

- Some weeds are known to have health benefits, for example Camomile.
- They can be stores of nectar for bees and food for other animals.
- They can help to stabilise and protect bare soil.

- Their strong tap roots can 'mine' deep lying mineral sources and bring them to the surface for the benefit of soil microbes; therefore they can help to correct soil mineral imbalances.
- These long tap roots also help to break up compacted soil.
- They can increase biodiversity.
- To the trained eye, weeds are indicators of the condition of the soil.

A *healthy* vegetative cover is essential for good soil. Therefore *certain* weeds can be better than nothing and indeed they often do many of the things that preferred plants do, apart from providing safe nutritious fodder for stock. Therefore, if the alternative is bare soil, weeds that do not cause health problems should only be removed when you are ready and able to replace them with a preferred species. In fact, out-competing weeds with a preferred species is usually a better approach than immediate removal, so that the land is *never* completely bare. You should, however, aim to prevent them from producing seed and spreading further.

Control of weeds

There are various strategies for dealing with weeds, ranging from minimum to maximum intervention, and often a combination of more than one strategy works best.

It always pays to seek local expert advice when tackling weeds.

Even if a property has good soil, you may still have weed infestations.

As a landowner/manager, you are expected to control weeds on your land, and usually on the area between your land and the road as well. There may even be a legal obligation in the case of certain noxious weeds. In most areas, there are 'statutory' requirements to ensure that certain weeds do not spread and threaten the wellbeing of other landowners, the community in general and the health of livestock. Check with your local authority/agriculture department about regulations

20

that will affect you and your land and to find out what is expected of you in your area. Below are some brief examples of the different strategies you can use, to control weeds but in addition always seek local expert advice.

Preventative measures

- **Avoid bare soil** on your land; bare soil is an invitation for weeds to become established. Good pasture management *is the best defence* against weeds.

Mechanical control

- **Mowing** *usually* favours grass plants rather than weeds and can reduce the seed setting of certain weeds if done at the right time i.e. before the seeds have ripened, otherwise you may simply be spreading seeds. Mowing is a good strategy for controlling tall weed plants, but is not usually effective for low growing plants as the blades will simply pass over the top of the plant.

Organic control

- **Cross grazing** with other animals can be very useful, especially sheep and goats which are more resistant to certain poisons in certain weeds. These animals are also invaluable for controlling woody/stemmy types of weeds such as blackberry and gorse (furze). Even chickens can be beneficial for weed control.
- **Hand pulling/hoeing by hand** which is very hard work but is a good strategy for small weed infestations and for keeping on top of areas that have previously been treated more aggressively. It must be done regularly to be effective. Rather than just pulling weeds out, always replace with seeds from a preferred species. Some plants, such as ragwort and and it relative, fireweed, are poisonous to hand pull as the toxins can be absorbed through the skin. Always wear gloves and in some cases a mask.

Chemical control

- **Most horse owners prefer not to use herbicides on their land** and, in many cases, they are not necessary. However, sometimes using herbicides to gain a quick advantage over certain weeds can be a good approach, if the plan is to introduce better, more organic, management in future. Always adhere to the instructions for use that are supplied with chemicals.

Whatever method of weed control you use, weed seeds **can remain in the soil for many years** even after you have removed *all* of the weed plants. These seeds will be waiting for their chance to re-establish themselves and this is why it is so important that you do not create bare soil. Vigilance is the key and you need to move swiftly on any new outbreaks.

Remember: healthy vigorous pasture plants are the best defence against weeds. The saying 'prevention is better than cure' could not be more true for weeds.

Healthy Land

Healthy pasture has many benefits for horses, the land/environment and ultimately for you – the horse owner.

Benefits for horses

- Grass and other pasture plants are what horses have evolved to eat; it is their most *natural* feed source. Horses eat a wide range of pasture species and, although predominantly grazers, they are also browsers and foragers, supplementing their diet with bushes, trees, herbs, berries and succulents.
- These pasture species have evolved over *millions* of years to have a *symbiotic* relationship with the animals that graze upon them. Just as the animals cannot survive without the nutrition that biodiverse pasture provides, the grasslands themselves are reliant on grazing animals for their survival.
- The *correct* type of pasture is an excellent feed source for most horses. Horses that are working very hard, lactating or growing may need supplementation with concentrate (hard) feed, but this is easily done. Even pasture that is deficient in certain nutrients can be remedied with the addition of supplements (minerals etc.). Horses that have a tendency to get overweight can be managed on pasture if care is taken and if the pasture in question is the 'right type'.
- Grazing horses are able to maintain the correct gut fill required to keep gastric ulcers at bay. Horses need and thrive on a very high fibre diet; without it their gut cannot function properly.

Grass and other pasture plants are what horses have evolved to eat.

- Grazing horses have their head down and are simultaneously draining their airways and breathing fresh air. This is very important as horses have delicate lungs which rely on the lowered head position to keep them clear.
- Pastured horses *generally* have a better quality of life than their stabled counterparts.
- Pastured horses have better circulation and better hoof quality due to the continual movement associated with grazing because,
- Pastured horses are exposed to sunlight, enabling them to synthesise enough vitamin D. This of course, is reliant on them not wearing rugs that block sunlight.

Benefits for land and the environment

- Pasture plants are a highly efficient 'carbon sink'. They take carbon out of the atmosphere and 'sink' it into the soil.
- Pasture plants collect and hold water, preventing the soil from drying immediately after morning dew and any rainfall.
- Pasture plants also slow the movement of water across the land, allowing it time to be absorbed into the soil and prevent erosion.
- As they grow, the roots of the plants allow air and water to penetrate the soil. Plants provide organic matter for soil; as their roots grow and die back in a continuous cycle, organic matter then builds up in the soil.
- Pasture plants cover, cushion and protect soil. Without this protection, soil becomes further compacted under the heavy weight of large grazing animals.
- Pasture plants hold soil together, protecting it from erosion. Without this protection, loose soil, along with manure, ends up in the waterways, causing pollution. This function is very important, as without soil and clean water nothing can survive.

Pasture plants collect and hold water.

Benefits for horse owners

- Pasture is a convenient and relatively cheap form of feed. Money spent on pasture renovation saves money spent on feed later. Pasture is up to ten times cheaper than the next cheapest form of feed – bought-in grass hay.
- Properties with good pasture have a higher value, therefore spending money and time on pasture management is a good investment if you own the land.
- If you lease the land than taking care of the pasture will also pay off, by making you a more favourable tenant.
- Horses at pasture are relatively easier to care for that horses that are yarded or stabled therefore the longer they can spend grazing the more time you will have to do other things with your horse/s.

Properties with good pasture have a higher value, therefore spending money and time on pasture management is a good investment if you own the land.

Biodiversity and horses

Biodiversity is vital for a healthy environment. Biodiversity, and all the benefits that go with it, is what you need to aim for on your land:

- A good, biodiverse pasture provides a wide variety of plants which contain different minerals and compounds, providing differing nutritional values and many health benefits for horses.
- In a natural ecosystem, there are many types of plants, animals and insects that live alongside each other and have symbiotic relationships, meaning that they cannot survive without each other.
- Increasing biodiversity, therefore, is not just about **taking care** of grazing animals and the plants that they eat, but it is also about providing habitat for numerous beneficial creatures ranging from insects to insectivorous (pest eating) birds etc.

- Horses, like all grazing animals, are excellent for the land when allowed to carry out their natural behaviours, and when they are managed in such a way that they are not allowed to overgraze an area.
- In many areas of the world horses are being used for the purpose of 'conservation grazing'. This practice, using domesticated and wild animals, aims to increase biodiversity in a given area.

Biodiversity is vital for a healthy environment.

Improving pasture

This section discusses the characteristics of suitable grasses for horses (because improving pasture may mean re seeding), and some simple things that you can do to turn land degradation around and improve your land.

Grasses for horses

The subject of grasses for horses is a *huge* subject. This section contains pointers to get you started. If you want to learn more there is some good information on this page of our website **www.equiculture.com.au/horses-and-pasture.html**
- If horses are allowed to eat too much high-energy (sugar) pasture, they can end up with laminitis or other obesity related disorders as a result.
- Laminitis in particular is a potentially devastating condition that can kill a horse or can certainly cripple a horse for life.

- A typical horse property may contain horses of varying size, age, workload and purpose, this makes it complicated when it comes to selecting grass types.
- In management terms it is easier and more cost effective to have paddocks containing *low* energy plants that *any* horse can eat safely and then *supplement* any horses that need it as and when, rather than having paddocks full of plants that are too high in energy.
- Beware of buying a standard 'horse pasture seed mix'. These mixes are often *too general* and may not even suit local conditions etc., in addition, they often contain the wrong kinds of grass seeds for horses.

A typical horse property may house horses that range significantly.

- Different pasture species have many values in a horse paddock. There is a huge range, even within a species, of how much NSC (sugars and starches) a plant can contain and it has much to do with the conditions that grass is grown in; always seek local advice, but look for low NSC (average 10% or less if possible), high-fibre grasses.
- It is possible to buy 'old fashioned' native/naturalised/ pasture seeds. They do tend to be expensive to buy compared to 'improved' species but they will save in the long run via healthier horses.
- Look to *encourage* 'old fashioned' native/naturalised grasses on your pasture. these types of plants are increasingly seen as the way forward for healthy horses.
- It is sometimes possible to collect desirable seeds from grasses that are growing around the outside of paddocks. Again, get local advice about when this should be done for the best results.

Land conservationists are a potential source of information about pasture plants. They will generally be in favour of conserving or recreating native or native/naturalised pasture and this type of pasture is generally what forward thinking horse owners want. If there is a land/soil conservation group (or similar) in your area, this can be a good place to start. They should be able to help identify plants on your land, whether they be native/naturalised or otherwise, and help you to obtain good seeds.

Simple solutions for turning land degradation around

Soil coverage

Check your pasture on a regular basis for ground coverage. A good time to do this is when you move the horses on to their next paddock (see the section **Rotational grazing**). Look down at the ground and make sure that there is *at least* 70% groundcover.

The area on the left below has too many bare patches for grazing and needs some TLC. The area on the right has good coverage.

Mulching

Any bare areas of soil can be covered with fine mulch while a paddock is resting, such as grass clippings - but be very careful that horses do not have access to them. Grass clippings can be very dangerous for horses to eat, if you did not already know this see this page on our website for more information **www.equiculture.com.au/horses-and-grass-clippings.html**.

Other forms of mulch can be old hay/straw, woodchips etc. **Mulching has various benefits:**
- It protects bare soil from the elements (wind and frost in particular).
- It also protects the soil from hoof pressure if animals are still in the area.
- It slows water down, holds it and allows it time to soak into the land.
- It provides habitat for beneficial fungi, worms and insects.
- It decomposes and provides a medium (new soil) for seeds to become established.

Mulching with round bales

- An easy way to mulch an area when hay is cheap and plentiful (and noxious weed free) is to feed grass hay round bales to a group of horses on any bare areas of soil in your paddocks.
- The hay needs to be made from a type of grass that you want on your land as it will contain seeds.
- Because it is being fed ad-lib the hay must also be low energy if the horses are prone to obesity and/or are not working.
- Any remaining hay left on the ground becomes mulch and provides all the benefits listed previously.
- This process works best with three to four horses as they will eat the round bale in about five to seven days. Less horses means that the bale may get rained on and develop mould, in this case the bale should be covered.

A great way to mulch an area when grass hay is cheap and plentiful is to feed clean grass hay round bales on bare areas to groups of horses. Inset: The decomposing mulch provides a medium for vegetation such as pasture plants to become established again.

- Even if it does not rain for a long time, the mulch is still doing a great job protecting the previously bare soil until conditions become right for mulch decomposition and subsequent plant growth.
- You will know when the horses have finished eating the edible parts of the bale, as they will start to hang around where they can see you. It is then time to put another bale on the next bare area, or to remove the horses from that area (or temporarily fence it off).

Using swales

Swales are barriers that are placed along the contours of the land. They can be made by simply placing items such as cut and laid vegetation, bundles of branches, old hay/straw bales, logs etc. on the ground. They divert water and are used to best effect *across* hillsides. They slow the water and give it more chance to soak into the soil. Loose soil and other organic matter such as leaves will build up behind the swale and this organic matter decomposes and creates soil for new plants to grow. Simply place swales on the ground in areas where the water moves fastest. Using swales, like mulching, is a very easy and inexpensive way of improving your land.

Swales are barriers, placed along the contours of the ground, that slow water and give it more opportunity to soak into the soil.

The same area a few weeks later. Initially weeds populated this area and then were replaced by grasses.

Pasture/grazing management

The section of this book called **The Equicentral System** addresses, and is a solution for, many of the land management issues covered so far in this book. However, in order to fully utilise this system, you first have to understand at least the basics about pasture/grazing management.

A basic rule of thumb for healthy productive land is that *no more than a third* of the available land should be in use at any one time, and the other two thirds should be being rested and allowed to recuperate.

Healthy land, healthy pasture, healthy horses...

Grazing systems

The various land management strategies outlined next (with the exception of set-stocking) should be used in conjunction with one another for best results.

Set-stocking

It is common practice on a horse property to have *all of the land* in use *all of the time*. This practice is called 'set-stocking' and it is *not* recommended as a good way to manage land. Set-stocking is a common practice on many horse properties whereby horses are either separated into individual ('private') paddocks and these paddocks are used continuously, *or* the horses *are* kept as a herd but have access to all of the land continuously. The incidence of 'horse-sick' pasture is usually linked to the practice of set-stocking the land (see the section **The 'dunging behaviour' of domestic horses**, in particular see the diagram in that section that shows the problems associated with poor land management).

Set-stocking is *not* recommended as a management practice because it can lead to unhealthy horses *and* unhealthy land.

The incidence of 'horse-sick' pasture is usually linked to the practice of set-stocking the land.

Rotational grazing

Having several smaller paddocks rather than one large paddock allows the use of pasture rotation. Horses can then be moved around the land as a herd. This strategy **should** be used by *all* land managers so that pasture gets a period without *any* grazing pressure so that it can rest and recuperate.

This practice is closer to what happens to pasture in the natural situation. In the natural situation animals move *around* the landscape which gives areas a break, allowing recovery from a grazing period. As a horse property is usually much smaller than the area that wild /feral grazing animals have available to them, a land manager has to step in and make sure that areas have time for rest and recuperation. This is where pasture rotation comes in.

As part of your rotational grazing strategy, horses should be allowed to graze a designated paddock when the plants have reached an average height of around 15cm to 20cm (6in to 8in). Once they have grazed the paddock down to an average height of around 5cm to 8cm (2in to 3in), they should be moved on to the next paddock.

Remember: if plants are continuously grazed until too short they will take longer to recover if and when conditions improve, they may also become totally exhausted and die out. Short/stressed plants are also relatively higher in sugar (per mouthful) so overgrazed pastures can be unhealthy for overweight or otherwise problematic horses in particular.

In short, if you want your land to produce as much healthy pasture as possible then you need to implement rotational grazing.

Rotational grazing implements the 30% rule. This means that you will have more healthy pasture, less or no weeds and less or no land degradation issues.

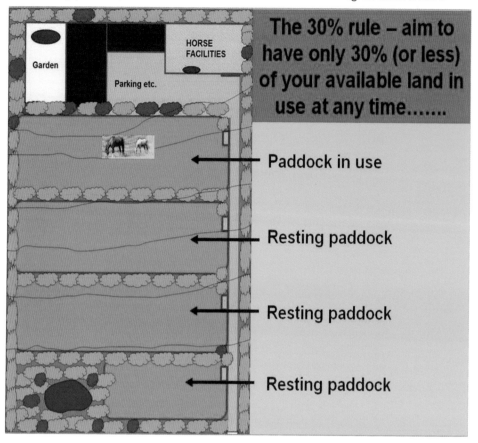

Limited grazing

The term 'limited grazing' means that you allow the horses to graze a designated paddock (as part of your rotational grazing system of management) for only *part of the time*. You might keep the horses confined either overnight or through the day for example. This strategy is carried out on a horse property for two main reasons: Firstly to reduce *grazing pressure* so that land does not become overgrazed, and secondly to reduce the pasture intake of horses, although this does not always work as intended - because the more you restrict a horse the more they tend to eat when allowed. For this reason you must always provide ad-lib fibre when a horse is removed from pasture - see this page of our website for more information **www.equiculture.com.au/feeding-confined-horses.html**

In some parts of the world horse owners also confine horses overnight for their safety due to the presence of wild/feral animals.

Limited grazing is an excellent strategy for reducing land degradation and for making your available pasture *last as long as possible*. As already mentioned, it may not be as effective at controlling your horse's intake, although if necessary, by reducing the turnout period significantly, and feeding low sugar hay instead, you can reduce their intake to some extent.

Limiting grazing and feeding hay in yards helps to improve land, which pays off in the future - for you - because it reduces feed costs, and for the horses - because it keeps the pasture healthier and means that it lasts longer throughout the year.

The importance of surfaced holding yards

On most horse properties, surfaced holding yards with shelters, or stables with attached outdoor yards are needed so that horses can be safely confined when necessary. For example, grazing time can then be increased when pasture is available and decreased when it is not.

Initially, a confinement area can be a 'sacrifice area' (see the next section); however it is a good idea to aim to build surfaced holding yards that also have shelter. If you have extreme weather conditions in your area you will need these as soon as possible. These yards will be invaluable when it is too wet, too dry etc.

If you are planning on building stables on your land consider instead building yards such as these because they are more 'horse friendly', and more versatile. They will probably cost about the same to build but they will be much more useful.

Aim to be flexible and be prepared to change what you are doing to suit the current situation i.e. a sudden but prolonged bout of heavy rain may mean that you have to increase the time the horses are held from the pasture. This means that the land is not damaged and it can resume full use much sooner. If necessary 'holding your horses' at the right time makes a huge difference to how much healthy pasture you have in the short *and* long term.

Holding yards can be a variety of shapes and sizes. These excellent holding yards with a large shelter can be opened out to be one large run-in shed (for a herd of horses), partitioned to make then into individual holding yards for single horses. They have all the uses that stables have plus many more.

'Sacrifice areas'

The term 'sacrifice area' means that part of the land is 'sacrificed' so that other areas have time to rest and recuperate. This would involve putting the horses in one paddock, or part of a paddock by using electric fencing, and allowing that area to be degraded (due to the high level of use), but keeping the majority of the land safe from degradation.

There are some things to keep in mind:

- As long as it is not too wet, an area of land can be used that is earmarked for pasture renovation later on.
- During drought conditions 'sacrifice areas' can be used to great effect if you 'mulch' the area at the same time, which may mean that the area comes out of the drought better than before (see the section **Mulching with round bales**).
- Only 'sacrifice' land if there are no other areas that could be used instead i.e. any land that already has 'hard standing' in place, such as an old farm yard.
- Sacrifice areas do not work well in wet conditions; the horses will quickly be standing in deep mud and you will have associated skin conditions and extensive soil degradation. In wet conditions, it is imperative that you try to use hard standing if you do not have a purpose built surfaced holding yard/s.
- Sacrifice areas should at best be considered a short term solution whilst more permanent holding yard structures are constructed.

The term 'sacrifice area' means that part of the land is 'sacrificed' so that other areas have time to rest and recuperate.

Strip grazing

This strategy involves using portable electric fencing to *reduce* the size of the area of the paddock currently available to the horses. By having their access restricted to a smaller area, the horses will graze more evenly on the available pasture and, at the same time, the fenced-off area is allowed to be in the *rest and recuperation phase* for longer, resulting in more pasture growth overall. Strip grazing is actually rotational grazing to an even greater degree.

Take care that you do not allow the area that is currently being grazed to be overgrazed. You still need to adhere to the same plant lengths as for normal rotational grazing (see the section **Rotational grazing**).

You can move the electric fence a set amount each day or you can simply divide a paddock into sections (and move it less often). Whatever you do will still result in more pasture being grown than if you do not strip graze. You can strip graze a long narrow paddock by putting the temporary fence in this position to start with...

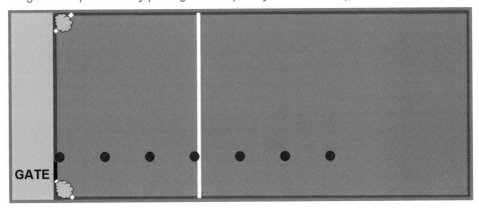

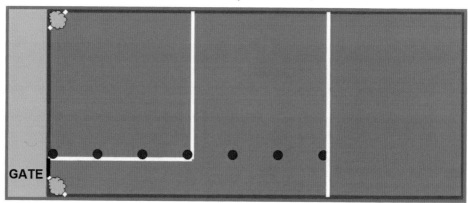

Cross grazing

'Cross grazing' is a term used to describe the practice of using more than one species of grazing animal to graze a pasture. Cross-grazing occurs naturally in the 'wild'. There are many benefits from utilising this management system if you can:

- Different animal species tend to complement each other in their grazing behaviours by eating different plants and different parts of the same plants, therefore more 'even' grazing, less weeds etc.

- Different grazing animal species will eat around the dung of other species, but not that of their own. Most parasitic worms of grazing animals are 'host specific' which means that they can only survive and carry out their life cycle in the animal species that they co evolved with. Therefore, when the 'wrong' animal picks them up, for example a cow picks up a horse worm, the worm dies.

There are a large amount of animals in this pasture but they are being moved on to the next paddock soon (rotational grazing). In this case the sheep are able to get out of the way of the horses if necessary by walking under the fence into the next 'cell'. Notice the even grazing (no 'roughs' or 'lawns').

If you are in the fortunate position of having too much pasture, consider getting a different animal species to graze the extra pasture rather than more horses as they will help you (and your horses) to produce healthier land. You may not need to *own* extra animals to get the benefits from cross grazing, your neighbours might own a different animal species to you so you may be able to allow them to occasionally graze your land and reap the rewards.

Fencing may be an issue as different animals have different fencing needs. Smaller animals, such as sheep and goats, must be able to get away from the horses is necessary. Some horses, young ones in particular, can be *very* rough with smaller animals.

Manure management

Manure can be used directly to aid soil conditioning. Horse people often feel that spreading manure on a horse paddock will lead to higher levels of parasitic 'worms' in their horses. *This is not necessarily true* if you manage your manure properly. There are several factors to keep in mind so that your soil gets the benefits of the manure without increasing the parasitic 'worm' burden of your horses.

Remember: the reason that people buy manure is to use it as a fertiliser and soil conditioner. By selling your horse manure you are robbing your land of organic matter and nutrients.

In some areas of the world, it is a legal requirement to collect, compost or dispose of horse manure. Always check local legislation before spreading manure on land.

Manure should be seen as black gold on a horse property for the following reasons:

- Horse manure can hold much more than its own weight in water. That fact alone makes it an important aid to retaining moisture in your soil.
- Horses excrete high levels of nutrients in their manure; well fed horses produce even higher levels of nutrients in their manure.
- Much of what horses consume contains high levels of indigestible fibre which is a good form of organic matter therefore horse manure is *very* high in organic matter. Many soils are low in organic matter so horse manure can help to redress this.

On a typical horse property you need to deal with manure that is collected from areas where horses are confined (such as yards and stables) and you may also be collecting manure from paddocks depending on your situation. So you need somewhere to store this manure (unless you are disposing of it immediately), in this case you might want to look at composting your manure.

Composting manure

Manure starts to decompose as soon as it is passed. One horse produces around 8-10 tons of manure per year, any bedding adds to this figure. Composting speeds up the process of decomposition that occurs naturally to everything organic. Bacteria and fungi consume oxygen while feeding on organic matter. This results in the release of heat, carbon dioxide and water vapour into the air. The end result of composting is a far superior product to 'fresh' manure. In addition to reducing your manure pile to half its original size and weight, composting destroys bacteria, diseases, weed seeds and parasitic 'worm' eggs in the process. Have a look at the page on our website about **horses and manure** for more information **www.equiculture.com.au/horses-and-manure.html**

Spreading composted manure:

- Spread it during the growing season so that plants can utilise it before it dries out/washes away. Composted manure is very valuable so make sure you get the best use out of it.
- If you are covering a bare soil area with composted manure cover the compost with old hay or some other form of mulch to prevent it drying out before it has chance to work.
- Spread it on the highest parts of your land so that more of your land benefits and to reduce the chances of it getting into any waterways. Therefore don't spread it on low lying/ permanently wet areas or anywhere it will wash into a waterway.

A good example of a three bay composting system with covers.

Paddock manure management

You must manage the manure in your paddocks to reduce the effects of the 'dunging behaviour' of horses. Picking up manure from larger paddocks is not usually necessary (or practical) if you carry out the good pasture management strategies that have been described so far in this publication plus the pasture maintenance strategies described next.

Pasture maintenance

Pasture maintenance is the name for routine procedures that may need to be carried out in order to maintain or improve the current condition of the pasture. Typically it includes mowing the remaining plants (after grazing and rotating the animals to the next pasture), harrowing manure or removing it and weed control (see the section **Weeds**). You may not need to do all or even any of these; it depends on your individual situation. This section goes through some of the pros and cons of mowing, harrowing and picking up manure and gives reasons for why you may or may not need to carry out these jobs.

Mowing

There are various terms used for the practice of cutting pasture plants, namely mowing, slashing and topping. Slashing and topping are the same thing, so for this section we will call it topping. The difference between topping and mowing is that topping simply cuts the plants once, leaving long stems lying on the ground, whereas mowing chops the plants (mulches them) into small pieces. The latter is usually preferable, as the cut plant then decomposes sooner. The smaller clippings fall between the stems that are left standing and do not impede their growth (as tall 'topped' grass can do until it decomposes), protecting any bare soil from the sun/wind and adding organic matter to the soil as they decompose. A tractor can be fitted with a topping or mowing implement (mowing implements usually cost more), whereas domestic lawn mowers and 'ride on' mowers mow.

Reasons to mow:

- Mowing 'grooms' the paddock, leaving it looking tidy.
- Mowing encourages pasture plants to thicken and improves soil coverage. This results in denser coverage, which means that each plant will receive relatively less sunshine once it regrows because, as the plants grow, the individual plants be closer together and will shade each other out. Therefore, the plants will be relatively lower in sugar/starch (NSC) and higher proportionately in fibre.
- Mowing allows sunlight to reach the base of the plants, giving shorter plants an opportunity to grow (as opposed to them being shaded out by taller plants).

- Organic matter (from the cut plants) ends up on the ground and decomposes to improve the soil, therefore mowing a pasture during a period of rapid growth can also be advantageous in terms of creating more organic matter for soil if this is needed.

There are many reasons to mow a pasture including it encourages pasture plants to thicken and improves soil coverage.

- At certain times of the year, you may have more pasture than your animals can handle, but cutting the plants does them good - it copies what happens to them in the natural grazing situation. Mowing puts plants back into the growing phase because once they go to seed, they stop growing, which creates more organic matter (both above and below ground). The pasture can be cut to any height between 5cm (2ins) and 10cm (4ins) in order to have a beneficial effect.
- Mowing also helps to control certain upright weeds (but not prostrate weeds), because many weeds do not thrive when cut back. Cutting a *grass* plant mimics the grazing of an animal and stimulates the plant to start growing again. Therefore, timely mowing favours grass plants and gives them a competitive advantage over many weeds (see the section **Control of weeds**).
- On a small horse property, a ride on mower is generally all that is required to tidy up a paddock, because the horses will have eaten the bulk of the plants before they are moved on to the next paddock (as part of a rotational grazing management system). Ideally, the plants should be cut at approximately 5cm (2.5ins) or higher. If a ride on mower is used, it must be set as high as possible because, unlike lawn type grasses, most pasture grasses do not cope with being cut too short.
- Cutting pasture plants with a machine helps to remove old, dry grass and encourages the growth of new fresh leaves, resulting in more uniform regrowth.

Mowing 'tidies up' the pasture and results in all of the plants having to regrow from the same starting height.

- Cutting pasture plants *just before* they set seed will encourage them to keep growing by keeping them in the elongation stage.
- Cutting any grass that is left behind *after* a grazing period is a way of artificially replicating what happens to plants in the wild situation. In the wild, herds of animals graze, trample and drop manure, but keep moving forward. The area then gets some rest and recuperation time before the next herd of animals, which are usually a different species, come along.
- Grass that is actively growing is actually 'safer' than grass that is too short or that has gone to seed. When using the word 'safer' here, we are speaking in terms of sugar and starch per mouthful, as the plant is using up its reserves of sugar and starch to grow. However, most horses will still need to have their intake monitored.

Why you might not need to mow:

- If you are cross grazing you may not need to mow because the other animal species will have grazed the paddock more evenly than if it had just been grazed by horses.
- If you only have a very small area of pasture and you are picking up manure, the 'roughs' may not become established and you *may* not need to mow.

How/when to mow:

- Your pasture should be mowed immediately after the horses have been moved on to the next paddock (as part of a rotational grazing management system). The remaining pasture should be cut to a height of about 5cm (2ins), level with the rest of the paddock, presuming that the horses were moved on when the paddock reached this stage. Even when you are using other animals, it may be beneficial to mow the paddocks periodically; it just will not be required as often.

Things to keep in mind are that:

- Take care if you are cutting a paddock that horses are currently grazing; if the plants are topped rather than mowed, the horses will probably leave the cut plants, preferring the shorter grass left behind. However, be aware that this pasture plant stubble may be relatively high in sugar/starch until it has chance to get growing again. If the horses do choose to eat the long pieces of cut plants, they still have to chew them.
- If the paddock is mowed instead, the very small pieces left behind may be eaten by the horses which can cause colic or even gut rupture (grass clippings can be very dangerous for horses, see this page on our website for more information **www.equiculture.com.au/horses-and-grass-clippings.html**).

41

- So, it is best to give the paddock at least few days rest after mowing to allow time for the clippings to either dry, out, wash into the soil or decompose to a point that the horses will not eat them.
- Generally speaking, it is best to only mow a paddock when horses have been moved on to the next paddock (as part of a rotational grazing management system).

Take care if you are cutting a paddock that horses are currently grazing.

Harrowing

Harrowing is a manure management strategy. It involves dragging an implement around land that has been grazed (and has manure piles in place) to break up the manure piles and spread them around the pasture. Harrowing is a controversial subject, with some people being wholeheartedly for it, and some being whole-heartedly against it. In reality, both sides of the argument are correct – in certain situations. This section will give you more information so that you can make up your own mind and decide whether it would suit your own management system.

Remember: if you do not do something with the 'roughs' in a paddock, these areas become unavailable as grazing areas and therefore tend to become larger over time. For example, a paddock that is five acres may end up having only three acres or less available for grazing. This compounds the nutrients in these areas, with the 'lawns' becoming increasingly depleted as horses take nutrients from them (by grazing them) and deposit them in the 'roughs' (in their manure).

Reasons to harrow:

- Spreading manure around a paddock rather than allowing it to stay in the areas that horses deposit it (the roughs) results in more uniform grazing in the future (see the section **The 'dunging behaviour' of domestic horses**). The whole paddock benefits from the nutrients and organic matter in the manure. The nutrients in uncomposted manure are not as available to plants as the nutrients in composted manure (see the section **Composting manure**), but it still means that they are better utilised than if they were left in the roughs.

Harrowing is a manure management strategy. It involves dragging an implement around land that has been grazed.

- Some people believe that harrowing is not a natural process, but in fact it is. In the natural situation, large herds of animals move across grassland and kick manure around with their hooves; harrows simply copy this process. Other species such as birds or beetles also spread the manure.
- Harrowing can help to kill some of the parasitic worms in the paddock. Breaking up manure dries it out and the eggs and larvae of parasitic worms need lots of moisture to survive, so when manure is drier *some* of the worms are killed. Strong sunshine or frost also kills some of the worms.
- Harrowing can also pull out any dead grass plants.
- Any subsequent rainfalls cause surviving parasite worm eggs to hatch. The larvae then climb to the top of grass stalks and wait to be eaten by a horse. If the paddock is being rested at this time (as it should be after harrowing as part of a rotational grazing management system), this causes *some* of the worm larvae to die as they do not survive in the larval stage outside of a horse for as long as they do as eggs.
- Some people believe that it causes horses to reject all of the paddock rather than just the 'roughs'. It is 'intact' piles of manure that horses avoid eating near

so, as long as manure is broken up, spread and then given time to wash into the soil, harrowing results in more even grazing in the future.

- Harrowing takes much less time than the regular picking up of manure.

Reasons not to harrow:

- If your local climate is mild for much of the year, it may not get hot, dry or cold enough to kill the parasitic worms before the horses are rotated back into the paddock in question. However the pasture itself benefits from spreading the nutrients.
- Some people enjoy picking up manure as they find it good exercise and therapeutic!
- If your grazing area is very small, harrowing might not be feasible. For example, if you rent a small paddock as is often the situation with livery, then you may not be able to rest areas of the paddock long enough to keep your horse/s safe from parasitic worms. In this case you will need to pick up manure from the land, see the section **Picking up manure in paddocks.**
- When **dung beetles**, the worlds class experts at dung management, are working.

How to harrow:

- Pasture harrows can be purchased in all shapes and sizes, they can also be home made. Homemade harrows can be constructed from many things such as from the springs of an old bed base, chain link fencing weighed down by tyres etc.
- The aim is to ensure that each and every pile of manure is broken up and scattered. If your land is not level, you need harrows that are flexible and can get into all the contours of your land. Commercial harrows usually have spikes that scratch the surface as spreading manure. This can pull out old dead plants and create grooves for new seeds to become established. But it is the manure spreading function that is the most important.
- Harrows can be pulled by a variety of vehicles ranging from a tractor to a four wheel drive, an ordinary car (in the right conditions) to a four wheel bike (for very lightweight harrows).
- Drive reasonably slowly otherwise the harrows will 'jump' over some of the piles.
- Make sure you store harrows in safe area; harrows are notorious for being left in paddocks and then forgotten about because the grass grows through them and then horses can inadvertently gallop through them when they are rotated back into that paddock!

When to harrow:

- The best time to harrow a paddock is after it has been grazed and the animals have been moved on to the next paddock, unless this coincides with a period of heavy rain. Heavy rain will wash harrowed manure off a paddock more easily than undisturbed manure. So if heavy rain is forecast, wait until it has been and gone before harrowing.

- It is also preferable to mow any long grass that has been left by the horses in the paddock *before* it is harrowed, because the harrows will then distribute this around the paddock at the same time as the manure.

- After mowing and harrowing, the paddock should be rested until the grass has reached an average height of 15cm to 20cm (6ins to 8ins), at which point the horses can be allowed to graze it again.

Dung beetles break manure down to a fibrous consistency.

Picking up manure in paddocks

Should you pick up manure from your paddocks or leave it? It comes down to whether you rotate your pastures or not. If you keep horses permanently in paddocks without rotating them around the available pasture then manure must be picked up (unless dung beetles are working). Conversely, it is not as necessary to collect manure in paddocks if the horses are rotated around the land. Harrowing and/or Cross grazing will also need to be carried out. Paddock rotation has huge benefits in terms of pasture and manure management, not least of all saving you time that would otherwise be spent picking up manure.

Therefore, collecting manure is necessary in paddocks that are set-stocked. Manure can either be picked up by hand (e.g. a shovel and wheelbarrow), or machines can be purchased that 'suck', 'sweep' etc. the manure. If you plan to buy such implements, make sure you do your homework first. They still require time and labour e.g. you still have to go out into the paddock with the machine! Ease of use should be very high on the list of priorities, because otherwise you may as well use the inexpensive 'old fashioned' method of a shovel and barrow.

In order to be effective against the formation of roughs and parasitic worm infestation, manure must be removed either daily or every two days at the most, (if other manure management strategies such as paddock rotation, harrowing and cross grazing are not being utilised). If manure is left any longer, the benefits of removing it decrease. The longer that manure is in the paddock, the more opportunity there is for equine parasitic worms to become established.

Further information

The subject of manure and what to do with it is a big one. See our **Horses and Manure** website page **www.equiculture.com.au/horses-and-manure.html** for much more information. On this page there are also links to other pages about **Horses and Dung Beetles** (the world class experts on natural dung management), **Horses and Chickens** (chickens can be useful when it comes to managing horse manure) and **Horses and Vermicomposting** (vermicomposting is the practice of using special composting worms to speed up the decomposition process).

Clean water on a horse property

Clean water is our **most important resource** therefore managing water on a horse property is a very important task. There are two main issues to consider. Firstly, getting the best use out of the water that arrives on your land. Secondly, ensuring that the water leaving your land is at least as clean, if not cleaner, than when it arrived so that you do not pollute the larger waterway system.

The water catchment

We all live in a water catchment therefore how we look after the water that passes through our land effects the local catchment area and beyond. In a healthy situation water passes through a **riparian zone** *before* it reaches a waterway. A riparian zone is a belt of dense vegetation that borders and surrounds a body of water (i.e. farm dam, lake, wetland, creek/stream or river). A *healthy* riparian zone is vital for clean water because the dense vegetation:

- Uses the nutrients that it captures to grow more vegetation - a win-win situation.
- Buffers the negative effects of floods and wind by holding the soil together and decreasing soil erosion.
- Shades the water, keeping it cooler and reducing evaporation.
- Provides habitat for wildlife, some of this wildlife eat pest insects and carry out various other important functions, such as plant pollination, that help to maintain a healthy ecosystem.

A healthy riparian zone filters sediments and nutrients that are washed off the land that would otherwise cause pollution in the waterway,

Many species of plants and animals live in a healthy riparian zone. It has deeper soil (from silt deposits) and supports a high level of biodiversity. Destruction of this zone through mismanagement has a major impact on water quality, both on your land and downstream of it, all the way to the sea.

The results of poor water management

Poor water management tends to go hand in hand with poor land management in general which results in bare, compacted soil and less pasture plants. It increases dust and mud which has a devastating effect on the water catchment. Areas of bare compacted soil *repel* rather than absorb water. When it rains the water runs over the ground rather than soaking in. This runoff takes soil and manure with it into the waterways. This rainfall is not available to your pasture (because it runs off rather than soaks in) which further reduces the pasture's ability to regenerate. In dry weather soil and dried out manure are blown of the land and some of this can end up in the waterways too.

All of this means that nutrients, bacteria, viruses and parasites enter the waterways and contaminate and pollute the water, causing big problems in the water system encouraging algae and aquatic weeds to form.

If horses are allowed to have direct access to waterways and riparian zones they have a damaging effect on them. Some of the problems include:

- Horses hooves cause soil (silt, clay and sand) to move around in the water which in turn can clog fish gills, cover spawning beds, smother fish eggs and make it hard for fish to see their prey. They fill in deep habitat holes that fish use to survive the heat of the day and hide from predators.

If horses are allowed to have direct access to waterways and riparian zones they have a damaging effect on them.

- This soil also coats in-stream vegetation and stops it from receiving the sun's rays.
- Dying plants and algae give off unpleasant odours and cause a drop in oxygen in the water which affects the fish's ability to breathe.
- Horses eat and trample seedlings and vegetation around waterways which reduces habitat for the wildlife that relies on them.
- Hooves compact the wet soils around the edge of waterways which suffocates plant roots and provides pockets of warm shallow water for mosquitoes and other pests to nest in.
- They pull out plants by the roots, which leads to bare soil and erosion. Erosion changes the course of creeks and rivers which leads to further erosion as the water moves faster (rather than meandering), taking more soil with it.
- Contaminated water is harmful for swimmers and if used by animals and people as drinking water. Even very small amounts of urine (ammonia) can be toxic to fish.

Grazing control around waterways

To prevent damage to the waterways by large grazing animals they need to be fenced off. Fencing enables the riparian (buffer) zone to grow undisturbed. Initially this fence can be a simple electric fence. Later the area can be fenced with more permanent materials. Take care to fence in such a way that native animals can still access the area (no low tight wires, no barbed wire). Speak with your local council, or environmental management group about the recommended distance that the fence should be from a waterway. It may be necessary to re-vegetate these areas if they are damaged to the point that they cannot re-vegetate themselves or if weeds have taken over. If weeds are a big problem care must be taken that their sudden removal does not result in further soil loss. You may have to remove weeds gradually while introducing more desirable species to the area. Find out and obtain the right planting list for your area by contacting a local native plant nursery or local environmental management group. But remember, you must fence first!

Clean water starts with either creating new riparian zones or protecting existing ones.

Vegetation on a horse property

Trees and bushes on a horse property carry out many vital functions both on a micro and macro scale. Aim for about 30% of your land to be covered with trees and bushes in order to benefit from their effects. Some of their functions include:

- They balance out the harsh extremes of the climate. When the weather is hot they provide shade for animals and people, they also reduce the reflective heat and cool the air temperature (through transpiration). When the weather is cold they provide shelter and hold heat in the area for longer.
- They provide habitat for wild animals which helps to maintain/create a natural ecosystem.
- When planted between paddocks (in particular on boundary fences) they are an aid to biosecurity, they reduce fence walking behaviour and prevent horses from playing over fences, therefore reducing fence injuries. Think of them as 'living fences' which once established perform many more functions than man made fences for a fraction of the cost!
- They bring nutrients up from far below the ground with their deep root systems and deposit these nutrients on the surface via their leaves when they fall and decompose. They also attract animals (birds and grazing animals) that drop manure in the area and add to this fertilising effect.
- They act as a windbreak and can slow down fire. They also trap dust and can reduce airborne weeds seeds spreading.

- They are an aid in drainage and help to control erosion. They slow the water that is travelling across your land and help to disperse it over a larger area.

When planted between paddocks (in particular on boundary fences) they perform many functions.

- They give privacy from neighbours and passing traffic and reduce noise pollution.
- They add value to a property by creating an attractive environment in which to live.
- They sequester carbon from the air and deposit it in the soil. By nurturing flora you are assisting in the reduction of carbon based pollutants in the atmosphere.
- Trees can provide an income or can be used on the property for firewood, fencing etc. There may also be an opportunity to receive an income from 'carbon offsetting'.
- They can provide feed for stock. Some trees and bushes can feed grazing animals as 'fodder trees'.
- They can give natural pest protection. Certain plants will repel insects.
- Some species such as legumes fix nitrogen from the air into the soil, thus helping other plants and the grass to grow by reducing the need to add fertiliser.
- When vegetation is planted next to waterway it shades the water and reduces evaporation when the weather is hot. This cleaner cooler water can then be reticulated (collected and distributed via tanks, pumps and troughs) around the property as and when needed.
- Large vegetation shades the paddock so that less sunshine gets to the pasture plants. This results in the plants being lower in sugar and starch. In the case of horses that are at risk of laminitis or have other metabolic and/or obesity related disorders this is a factor that can help with their management.

Trees and bushes add value to a property by creating an attractive environment in which to live.

Existing vegetation

Often these areas are seen as a nuisance on a horse property and are earmarked for clearance but they should be seen as a valuable asset. In particular if these areas are high up on your land they help to fertilise areas below them both by bringing nutrients up from deep within the soil and depositing them on the surface via their leaves and by attracting animals such as wildlife/birds etc. which drop manure in the area. These nutrients then make their way downhill via gravity and water. These areas need to be fenced off to protect them from large grazing animals. If possible these areas should link with other remnant vegetation areas and fenced off waterways on your land and outside the property to maintain/create wildlife corridors. Any fencing should allow native animals to pass through. Try to leave fallen trees in these areas if safe to do so as they provide good habitat for wildlife.

Protection and care of trees and plants

Trees and plants need protection from livestock if they are to survive and thrive. A healthy tree or plant will be able to resist pests and diseases far better than one that is compromised. Horses will often 'ringbark' trees by chewing off the bark, killing the tree. This often occurs if a horse's diet is lacking in fibre. If allowed too near a tree, horses and other large grazing animals seeking shade will compact the ground around the roots. Horses (and other animals) rub on and chew/pull out young trees, making it difficult for them to get established.

Plant new trees in areas where horses do not have access. By fencing off waterways and remnant vegetation and by planting new trees/bushes between paddocks, in laneways, between yours and your neighbours property and around buildings, stables and yards you will find that it is easy to achieve the figure 30% of your property being vegetated with trees and bushes.

Protect new plantings from livestock.

Putting it all together

The use of various land, manure, water and vegetation management strategies offers great results for all concerned. If this all seems a little complicated, try to remember that rotational grazing is the main management strategy you should use. Pasture **must** have periods where it is allowed to rest and recuperate and therefore all land managers need to use this strategy so that paddocks get periods without any grazing pressure at all.

Remember - the aim is to have healthy, vigorous plants, not stressed, worn out plants. The other grazing management strategies such as limited grazing, strip grazing and cross-grazing are used in conjunction with rotational grazing to 'fine tune' grazing pressure.

The use of various land, manure, water and vegetation management strategies offers great results for all concerned.

The Equicentral System

The Equicentral System is a *total* horse and land management system that we have developed and have been teaching to horse owners around the world for many years now. It uses the natural and domestic behaviour of horses, combined with good land management practices, to create a healthy and sustainable environment for your horses, the land that they live on *and* the wider environment.

There are many examples in various countries including Australia, New Zealand, the UK, the USA and even Panama! This list just keeps growing as people realise the huge benefits of using **The Equicentral System** in order to manage their horses in a sustainable way.

How The Equicentral System works

The Equicentral System utilises the natural grazing and domestic paddock behaviour of horses in order to benefit the land that they live on *and* the wider environment. In turn this benefits the horses and it also benefits you (and your family) because it saves you money and time/labour.

- The main facilities – water, shade/shelter, hay and any supplementary feed are positioned in a surfaced holding yard so that the horses *can always* get back to them from the pasture they are currently grazing.
- The watering points are *only situated in the surfaced holding yard*, instead of there being one in each paddock. If you already have water troughs' situated in paddocks these can be turned off when horses are using the paddock, and turned back on again if and when other animals, such as cows or sheep, are grazing there.
- Individual water troughs/drinkers (or buckets) of course are also needed in any individual yards/stables.
- If possible all of the paddocks *are linked* to this surfaced holding yard area, although only one paddock is in use at any time.
- The gate to the paddock that is currently in use *is always* open, so that the horses *can always* get themselves back to the water/shade/shelter etc. *In short, the horses are never shut out of the surfaced holding yard*.
- Occasionally they may be fastened in the surfaced holding yard (with hay), but this is usually for the purpose of preventing damage to the land and increasing healthy pasture production.
- Apart from trees or bushes that are situated in/around paddocks, *the only shade/shelter is in the surfaced holding yard*. This shade/shelter is very important. It should be large enough for the whole herd to benefit from it at the same time.

*The **Equicentral System**: all of the paddocks lead back to the surfaced holding yard. There is shade/shelter and water in this central area. Hay can also be fed here.*

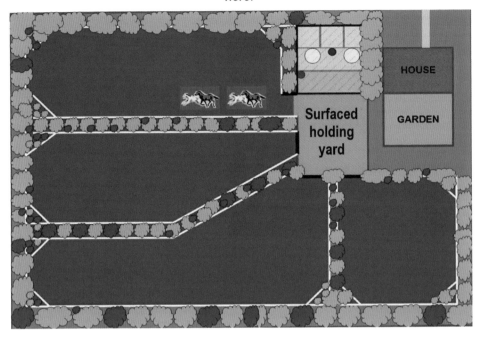

Additional information

- The surfaced holding yard area *can* also be a riding/training surface if that is what you wish. You may prefer to keep it separate or indeed you may not need a riding/training surface - but if you do then this means that the expense of creating this surfaced area has double benefits. This could mean that you are able to afford and justify this surfaced area sooner because you are going to get more use out of it. Also remember, the smaller the horse property, the more the facilities need to be dual purpose whenever possible so that you have as much land in use as pasture as possible.
- Careful consideration of the surface is required, especially if it is to be a riding/training surface as well. Remember - bare dirt is not an option. Wet mud is dangerously slippery and can harbour viruses and bacteria which can affect the horses legs. Mud will become dusty when dry, meaning that the horses will be breathing in potential contaminants *and* you will be losing top soil.
- It is useful if there are also some individual holding yards (or stables if you already have them) – preferably linked to the surfaced holding yard for ease of use. You can then separate horses into them for any individual attention that they may require (such as grooming, supplementary feeding etc.) or for tacking

up etc. You can also put the surplus horses in them if you are riding/training one of the herd members on the larger surfaced holding yard.

The surfaced holding yard area can also be a riding/training surface if that is what you wish. If you do then this means that the expense of creating this surfaced area has double benefits.

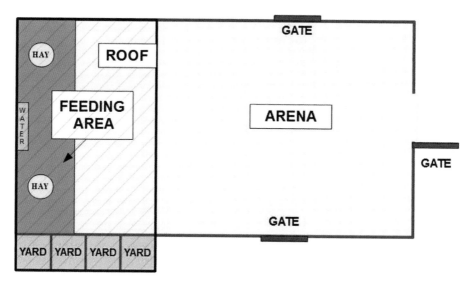

- This system is ***not*** about food restriction – quite the opposite. It is about transitioning horses to an ad-lib feeding regime of low energy pasture plants and hay so that they no longer gorge and put weight on because of it. See our books **The Equicentral System Series Book 1 – 3** (listed at the end of this book) for information about how to do this.
- Your pasture may need to be transitioned to lower energy plants. This does not always mean reseeding.
- Hay can be fed in the larger surfaced holding yard if the horses get on well enough; generally horses will share hay. Otherwise, it can be fed in the individual holding yards/stables, but keep in mind that there should *always* be some form of feed available to the horses
- It can be a good idea to create a feeding area in the larger surfaced holding yard using large rubber mats or similar.
- **The Equicentral System** works best on a property where the horses live together as one herd, otherwise you will need to replicate it for each group of horses that you have. However, many of our clients have done just that in the case of larger properties with various classes of horses (for example studs, livery yards etc.).

- **The Equicentral System** assumes that you already have good grazing management in place (rotational grazing) or that you plan to implement it. Remember, rotational grazing involves moving the animals around the land as a herd, one paddock at a time, rather than allowing them access to all of the available land area at once (set-stocking).

It is useful if there are also some individual holding yards (or stables if you already have them) – preferably linked to the surfaced holding yard for ease of use. These individual yards can be made from swing away partitions if you only require them periodically (picture left) or can be permanently in place (picture right).

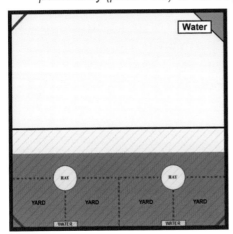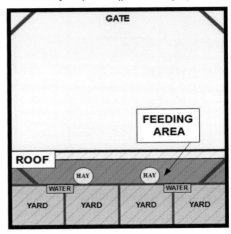

This is an example of how **The Equicentral System** works in practice. In this example, the horses are being kept in the surfaced holding yard at night (or in individual holding yards/stables) and out at pasture through the day, but remember - if there is enough pasture, then the horses do not need to be confined overnight unless you have other reasons for doing so.

- In the morning you open the surfaced holding yard/riding arena gate and the horses **walk themselves** to the paddock that is currently in use for a grazing bout (which lasts between 1.5 to 3 hours), the gate to this paddock should already be open (the other paddocks should have closed gates as they are being rested).
- At all times the horses are free to return to the surfaced holding yard for a drink, but they usually won't bother until they have finished their grazing bout.
- After drinking, the shade and inviting surface in the surfaced holding yard encourages the horses to rest (loaf) in this area before returning to the paddock for another grazing bout later in the day.
- Leaving hay in the surfaced holding yard can encourage even more time being spent (voluntarily) in the surfaced holding yard and less time spent in the paddock.

- At the end of the day, the horses return from the paddock to the surfaced holding yard to await you and any supplementary feed that they may be receiving.

After a grazing bout, the horses return to the surfaced holding yard for a drink.

- You simply close the gate preventing them from returning to the paddock for the night, or, if conditions allow it, the horses can come and go through the night as well as through the day.

After drinking, the shade and inviting surface in the surfaced holding yard encourages the horses to rest (loaf) in this area before returning to the paddock for another grazing bout later in the day.

The Equicentral System benefits

The Equicentral System utilises the natural and domestic behaviour of horses to better manage the land that they live on. This system of management has many, many benefits including:

Horse health/welfare benefits

The Equicentral System has numerous health and welfare benefits:

- It encourages horses to move more and movement is good; a grazing horse is a moving horse. A recent (Australian) study showed that horses in a 0.8 Ha. paddock walked approximately 4.5km per day, even when water was situated in the paddock; additional movement to the water in the surfaced holding yard, therefore, further increases this figure. More movement also means better hoof quality as the hooves rely on movement to function properly. Remember a healthy, biodiverse pasture encourages more movement.

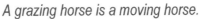

A grazing horse is a moving horse.

- It *maximises* time spent grazing for horses and aims to avoid food restriction. By confining horses initially and when the weather is very dry or very wet (or in order to transition horses that have been on restricted diets in the past), so that the pasture begins to improve, becomes more biodiverse etc. they will be able to graze more in the future because healthy pasture can withstand more grazing.

- Horses are not being forced to stand in mud, especially around gateways when weather conditions are wet. Horses are not good at coping with continuous wet conditions – hence the ease with which they develop skin conditions such as greasy heel/mud fever. Remember - in the naturally-living situation, they will *take themselves* to higher, dryer ground to loaf, even if the areas that they graze are wet. When horses are fastened in wet paddocks, they do not have this choice.

The horses will be able to graze more in the future because healthy pasture can withstand more grazing.

- Eliminating mud also means eliminating dust because they derive from the same thing (bare soil) at either end of a spectrum. Apart from the obvious benefits to not losing your top soil, this means that horses (and humans) do not have to cope with living in a dusty environment.
- Horses move around a paddock in a natural fashion, choosing what to eat. As rotational grazing increases the diversity of plants in a pasture, the horses benefit from access to a larger variety of plants. This means that the horses eat a more natural, varied diet. In addition, healthier plants are safer to graze than stressed, overgrazed plants (more fibre and less sugar per mouthful).
- The stress of not being able to get to food at will, along with all of its associated problems, is removed. Horses with different dietary requirements can be catered for with the addition of supplementary daily feed (in a separate but preferably adjoining area).
- The surfaced holding yard is seen by the horses as a good place to be and therefore, if and when it is necessary to fasten them in there, (bad weather, for the vet etc.) they are not stressed.
- The horses now have choice; they can choose as a herd whether to graze, walk to the 'water hole', snooze in the shade etc. Instead of us deciding when a grazing bout will start/finish, the horses can decide for themselves. These are all behaviours that naturally-living horses take for granted, but domestic horses are

usually 'micro managed' in such a way that a human decides where they will be at any point in the day. This might not seem like a big deal but it really is.

The Equicentral System provides a 'home-range' whereby the horses can access the available resources in a more natural fashion.

Time saving benefits

The Equicentral System has various time saving benefits:

- You do not have to lead horses in and out to the pasture. The horses are waiting for you close to the house, or at least in an area where you need them to be, much of the time. If they are currently grazing, you simply call them; horses soon learn to come to a call for a reward. This means that when you return from work and the weather is bad, you do not need to trail out in the wind and the rain to bring them in, they will be waiting for you in the surfaced holding yard.
- You do not have to spend time carting feed around the property (or keep a vehicle especially for the job) because the horses *bring themselves* to the surfaced holding yard for feed. The horses *move themselves* around the property, *taking themselves* out to the paddock that they are currently grazing, and bringing *themselves* back for water and feed.
- The single water trough in the surfaced holding yard is all that you have to check each morning and night, saving you having to go out to a paddock and check the water.
- It is far quicker to pick up manure from the surfaced holding yard than from pasture if you collect your manure.
- Any time you save can be spent on other horse pursuits such as exercising them!

You do not have to spend time carting feed around the property.

60

Cost saving benefits

The Equicentral System has various cost saving benefits:

- Money spent on the surfaced holding yard is money well spent, as this area is used *every day of the year* for *at least twelve hours* a day, even if you are not also using this surface for riding/training.
- Money spent on vet bills for treating skin and hoof conditions is reduced or totally eliminated.
- The expense of installing and/or maintaining a water trough in each paddock is spared.
- The expense of installing individual shade/shelters in each paddock is spared. Instead, one large shade/shelter is erected at the side of or over the surfaced holding yard, which means you may end up with a partially covered all weather riding/training surface if you are multi-tasking this area!
- This large shade/shelter will be in use *every day* of the year, unlike shade/shelters that are situated in paddocks and are only in use when the paddock is in use. Remember - if you are rotating your paddocks (as part of a rotational grazing management system), then this means that each paddock will be empty, and any shade/shelters situated in them will be unused, for a large part of each year.
- Annual maintenance including time and expense, of numerous shelters (especially if they are made of wood) is avoided adding to the cost effectiveness of **The Equicentral System**.

This large shade/shelter will be in use every day of the year, unlike shade/shelters that are situated in paddocks and are only in use when the paddock is in use.

- Many horse properties already have the facilities required to implement **The Equicentral System**. Often the required infrastructure either already exists on a horse property, or the property needs minimal changes.
- Laneways (and their associated costs) can be kept to a minimum. In areas that *do* require laneways, any money spent on surfacing them is well utilised as the laneways will be used by the horses several times a day.
- Better land management means more pasture to use for grazing (and safer healthier pasture) and more opportunities for conserving pasture (as 'standing hay' for example) or making hay. This all leads to much less money being spent on bought-in feed.
- You do not need to buy and maintain a vehicle for 'feeding out'. The horses come to where the feed is stored rather than you having to trail around the paddocks 'feeding out'.
- Setting up **The Equicentral System** will not devalue your land. It will actually increase the value of it through good land management. Likewise, if you sell the property, the next owner can choose to set up a more traditional management system by putting water and shade/shelter in every paddock if they wish.

Safety benefits

- Horses move themselves around the land, therefore there is less unnecessary contact between humans and horses. This is an important point if you have (usually less experienced) family or friends taking care of your horses when you are away. **The Equicentral System** allows them to see to your horses without them having to catch and lead them around the property.
- It reduces or eliminates the incidence of horses and people being together in a paddock gateway. When horses are led out to a paddock, they can be excited because they are about to be freed; and when they are waiting at a gate to come back in for supplementary feed, they are keen to get through the gateway in the other direction for their feed. Horses can crowd each other and human handlers can become trapped. These situations are very high risk on a horse property.
- Depending on its position, the surfaced holding yard can be a firebreak (for your home) and a relatively safe refuge in times of fire/storm/flood for your horses. The layout of the property may result in the horses being pushed (by rising water) back towards the surfaced holding yard in a flood. Assuming the surfaced holding yard is built on higher ground, this can save lives! By training the horses to always come back on a call, you can get them into the surfaced holding yard quickly in any emergency situation. This makes it far easier for you, your neighbours, or the emergency services to evacuate your horses if necessary in emergency situations.

Land/environmental management benefits

The Equicentral System is a *sustainable* system that acknowledges that a horse is *part of* an ecosystem, not separate to it. There are many benefits associated with this approach:

- **The Equicentral System** complements a rotational grazing land management system and allows for the fine tuning of it. Remember - rotational grazing encourages healthy pasture growth and aids biodiversity by moving the animals to the next grazing area before they overgraze some of the less persistent plant varieties.
- With good land management, the productivity of biodiverse, safer pasture should *increase* rather than decrease over time, leading to fewer periods when it is necessary to fasten horses in the surfaced holding yard over time. Remember - biodiversity is good for horses *and* good for the environment.
- It *vastly* reduces land degradation that would be caused by unnecessary grazing pressure. The horses *voluntarily* reduce their time spent on the pasture. They will tend to spend the same amount of time grazing (as they would if they were fastened in a paddock for 24 hours), but will tend to carry out any other behaviours in the surfaced holding yard.

They will tend to carry out any other behaviours in the surfaced holding yard.

- They prefer the surfaced holding yard not least because, if it is situated near the house, or at least in an area that they can see you coming towards them, no self-respecting horse will miss an opportunity to keep watch for the possibility of supplementary feed! The water and shade in the surfaced holding yard also encourages the horses to loaf in this area. If the horses are allowed to come and go night and day they will reduce the grazing pressure (grazing pressure being a combination of actually eating but also standing around on the land) by approximately 50%. If you fasten them in the surfaced holding yard (with hay) overnight, you will further reduce the grazing pressure by about another 50% (making a total of about 75%). This reduction in grazing pressure will make a *huge* difference to the land.
- The corresponding compacted soil/muddy areas that surround water troughs and paddock shelters, as well as the tracks that develop in a paddock are avoided. Bare/muddy/dusty gateways are also a thing of the past as horses are *never* fastened in a paddock waiting to come in. Don't forget that the idea is to reduce any unnecessary pressure on your valuable pasture and increase movement. Remember - the reason horses stand in gateways is because that is usually the nearest point to supplementary food; they are either fed in that area or their owner leads them from there to a surfaced holding yard or stable to feed them. If the gate is closed, they stand there; if the gate is open, they bring themselves into the surfaced area, which becomes their favourite loafing area.
- It reduces the area of land used for laneways and therefore the land degradation caused by them – by minimising laneways as much as possible. This is done by creating a layout whereby the paddocks lead directly to the surfaced holding area or by creating temporary laneways. If paddocks are already fenced and laneways are in place then this system utilises them efficiently and safely i.e. the horses are not fastened in narrow areas, they can spread out when they reach the paddock at one end or the surfaced holding yard at the other.
- It increases water quality – by minimising or eliminating soil and nutrient runoff. Rotational grazing maintains better plant cover – the absolute best way to keep soil and nutrients on the land and out of the waterways.
- Strip grazing is usually easier to set up because the water point is back in the surfaced holding yard, meaning that the fence only has to funnel the horses back to the gate, without having to take the water trough position into consideration.
- Hay is fed in the surfaced holding yard area rather than the paddocks allowing for better weed control.

Public perception benefits

The Equicentral System helps to create a positive image of horsekeeping. There are various reasons for wanting to do this:

- **The Equicentral System** is most likely to be regarded as a good way to manage land by landowners, the general public and the local authorities. There is a general expectation that land should be well managed - i.e. less mud/dust and fewer weeds rather than more mud/dust and weeds.
- **The Equicentral System** fulfils this expectation, creating a positive image of horse ownership rather than a negative one. This is an important point, remember - in some areas legislation is being pushed forward to reduce horsekeeping activities due to the negative image caused by the often poor land management practices on many horse properties.
- In particular, as horses are often kept on land that is leased rather than land that is owned by the horse owner, the landowner usually, and quite rightly, expects to see good land management taking place. Of course horse owners that own their own land should, and usually do, want the same.

There is a general expectation that land should be well managed - i.e. less mud/dust and fewer weeds.

Manure and parasitic worm management benefits

The manure, along with the horses, comes to you. More manure is dropped in the surfaced holding yard and much less in the paddocks (as much as 75% less if you fasten the horses in the surfaced holding yard/s at night with hay). This allows for much better manure management:

- If you usually collect manure that is dropped on pasture then it is physically easier to pick up manure from the surfaced holding yard/s.

- This collected manure can then be composted (which also reduces parasites on your land, as thorough composting can kill parasitic worm eggs and larvae).
- Composted manure is much better 'product' than 'fresh' manure.
- Less manure on the pasture is less importunity for parasitic worm larvae to attach to pasture plants.
- Better manure management also means less reliance on worming chemicals.
- The extra pasture created by managing the land better increases the possibility of being able to 'cross-graze' (graze other species of animals on the land). This further reduces parasitic worms on the land in the most natural way possible, because parasitic worms are what is termed 'host specific', meaning that they can only survive when picked up by the host animal that they evolved alongside.
- Rotational grazing also aids in parasitic worm management by increasing the time that a given area of pasture is resting, which means that *some* of the parasitic worm larvae (on the pasture) dry out and die as they wait - in vain! - for a horse to eat the plant that they are attached to.

Manure dropped on the surfaced yard rather than pasture is also far preferable in terms of parasitic worm management (no plants for any larvae that hatch out to attach to).

See **The Equicentral System Series Book 1 – 3** (see the end of this book) for much more information about **The Equicentral System** including how to implement it in various situations including: on very small and larger areas of land, in different climates, on land that you lease, in a livery/agistment/boarding situation and in a 'private paddock' situation. Also, how to utilise any existing facilities or how to start from scratch. Finally, why and how to minimise laneways and how to set up temporary laneways if necessary. These books also have information about changing a horse from a restricted diet to an ad-lib diet (high fibre/low sugar).

Summary of the main points

- **Healthy Land = Healthy Pasture = Healthy Horses.**

- **To manage your land well** it is essential to learn about certain normal/natural and abnormal/unnatural horse characteristics and behaviours.

- **Horses are herbivores**; they eat plants and lots of them. This natural food source for horses is low in calories and takes a long time to collect, chew and digest.

- **Acid continuously builds up in the stomach of a horse.** The acid in the stomach is usually buffered by the saliva that the horse swallows while chewing fibrous material.

- **While a horse is grazing, they are also walking** because the plants are stationary and the horse has to keep moving in order to graze them.

- **In the naturally-living situation, horses will never stand for hours in mud**, instead, they will take themselves to a higher, drier area.

- **The easily visible signs of land degradation** are 'horse sick' pasture, bare soil, soil erosion, dust, mud, weed infestations and dead or dying trees.

- **Whenever horses are not grazing, they should carry out all other behaviours in an area that is created for that purpose** and, if possible, they should be able to take themselves to that area.

- **Weeds tend to be strong competitors**, moving in when conditions favour them, especially when the soil is bare or in poor condition.

- **Land conservationists** are a potential source of information about pasture plants.

- **You must manage the manure** in your paddocks to reduce the effects of the 'dunging behaviour' of horses.

- **Clean water is our most important resource** therefore managing water on a horse property is a very important task.

- **Trees and bushes on a horse property carry out many vital functions** both on a micro and macro scale. Aim for about 30% of your land to be covered with trees and bushes in order to benefit from their effects.

- **The Equicentral System is a total horse and land management system**. It uses the natural and domestic behaviour of horses, combined with good land management practices, to create a healthy and sustainable environment for your horses, the land that they live on and the wider environment.

Further reading - A list of our books

Buying a Horse Property

Buying a horse property is probably the most expensive and important purchase you will ever make. Therefore, it is very important that you get it right. There are many factors to consider and there may be compromises that have to be made. This guide to buying a horse property will help you to make many of those very important decisions.

Decisions include factors such as whether to buy developed or undeveloped land? Whether to buy a smaller property nearer the city or a larger property in a rural area? Other factors that you need to think about include the size and layout of the property, the pastures and soil, access to riding areas, the water supply, and any possible future proposals for the area. These subjects and many more are covered in this book. A useful checklist is also provided so that you can ask the right questions before making this very important decision.

If you are buying a horse property, you cannot afford to miss out on the invaluable information in this book!

The Equicentral System Series Book 1: Horse Ownership Responsible Sustainable Ethical

With horse ownership comes great responsibility; we have a responsibility to manage our horses to the best of our ability and to do this sustainably and ethically.

Horse keeping has changed dramatically in the last 30 to 40 years and there are many new challenges facing contemporary horse owners. The modern domestic horse is now much more likely to be kept for leisure purposes than for work and this can have huge implications on the health and well-being of our horses and create heavy demands on our time and resources. We need to rethink how we keep horses today rather than carry on doing things traditionally simply because that is 'how it has always been done'. We need to look at how we can develop practices that ensure that their needs are met, without compromising their welfare, the environment and our own lifestyle.

This book brings together much of the current research and thinking on responsible, sustainable, ethical horsekeeping so that you can make informed choices when it comes to your own horse management practices. It starts by looking at the way we traditionally keep horses and how this has come about. It then discusses some contemporary issues and offers some solutions in particular a system of horsekeeping that we have developed and call **The Equicentral System.**

For many years now we have been teaching this management system to horse owners in various climates around the world, to great effect. This system has many advantages for the 'lifestyle' of your horse/s, your own lifestyle and for the wider environment - all at the same time, a true win-win situation all round.

The Equicentral System Series Book 2: Healthy Land, Healthy Pasture, Healthy Horses

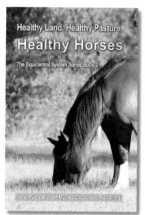

If you watch horses grazing pasture, you would think that they were made for each other. You would in fact be correct; millions of years of evolution have created a symbiotic relationship between equines (and other grazing animals) and grasslands. Our aim as horse owners and as custodians of the land should be to replicate that relationship on our land as closely as possible.

In an ideal world, most horse owners would like to have healthy nutritious pastures on which to graze their horses all year round. Unfortunately, the reality for many horse owners is far from ideal. However, armed with a little knowledge it is usually possible to make a few simple changes in your management system to create an environment which produces healthy, horse friendly pasture, which in turn leads to healthy 'happy' horses.

Correct management of manure, water and vegetation on a horse property is also essential to the well-being of your family, your animals, your property and the wider environment.

This book will help to convince you that good land management is worthwhile on many levels and yields many rewards. You will learn how to manage your land in a way that will save you time and money, keep your horses healthy and content *and* be good for the environment all at the same time. It is one of those rare win-win situations.

The Equicentral System Series Book 3: Horse Property Planning and Development

It does not matter if you are buying an established horse property, starting with a blank canvas or modifying a property you already own; a little forward planning can ensure that your dream becomes your property. Design plays a very important role in all our lives. Good design leads to better living and working spaces and it is therefore very important that we look at our property as a whole with a view to creating a design that will work for

our chosen lifestyle, our chosen horse pursuit, keep our horses healthy and happy, enhance the environment and to be pleasing to the eye, all at the same time.

Building horse facilities is an expensive operation. Therefore, planning what you are going to have built, or build yourself is an important first step. Time spent in the planning stage will help to save time and money later on.

The correct positioning of fences, laneways, buildings, yards and other horse facilities is essential for the successful operation and management of a horse property and can have great benefits for the environment. If it is well planned, the property will be a safer, more productive, more enjoyable place to work and spend time with horses. At the same time, it will be labour saving and cost effective due to improved efficiency, as well as more aesthetically pleasing, therefore it will be a more valuable piece of real estate. If the property is also a commercial enterprise, then a well-planned property will be a boon to your business. This book will help you make decisions about what you need, and where you need it; it could save you thousands.

Horse Rider's Mechanic Workbook 1: Your Position

Many common horse riding problems, including pain and discomfort when riding, can be attributed to poor rider position. Often riders are not even aware of what is happening to various parts of their body when they are riding. Improving your position is the key to improving your riding. It is of key importance because without addressing the fundamental issues, you cannot obtain an 'independent seat'.

This book looks at each part of your body in great detail, starting with your feet and working upwards through your ankles, knees and hips. It then looks at your torso, arms,

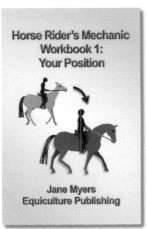

hands and head. Each chapter details what each of these parts of your body should be doing and what you can do to fix any problems you have with them. It is a step by step guide which allows you to fix your own position problems.

After reading this book, you will have a greater understanding of what is happening to the various parts of your body when you ride and why. You will then be able to continue to improve your position, your seat and your riding in general. This book also provides instructors, riding coaches and trainers with lots of valuable rider position tips for teaching clients. You cannot afford to miss out on this great opportunity to learn!

Horse Rider's Mechanic Workbook 2: Your Balance

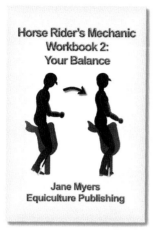

Without good balance, you cannot ride to the best of your ability. After improving your position (the subject of the first book in this series), improving your balance will lead to you becoming a more secure and therefore confident rider. Improving your balance is the key to *further* improving your riding. Most riders need help with this area of their riding life, yet it is not a commonly taught subject.

This book contains several lessons for each of the three paces, walk, trot and canter. It builds on **Horse Rider's Mechanic Workbook 1: Your Position**, teaching you how to implement your now improved position and become a safer and more secure rider. The lessons allow you to improve at your own pace, in your own time. They will compliment any instruction you are currently receiving because they concentrate on issues that are generally not covered by most instructors.

This book also provides instructors, riding coaches and trainers with lots of valuable tips for teaching clients how to improve their balance. You cannot afford to miss out on this great opportunity to learn!

You can read the beginning of each of these books (for free) on the on the Equiculture website www.equiculture.com.au

We also have a website just for Horse Riders Mechanic www.horseridersmechanic.com

Our books are available in various formats including paperback, as a PDF download and as a Kindle ebook. You can find out more on our websites where we offer fantastic package deals for our books!

Final thoughts

Thank you for reading this book. We sincerely hope that you have enjoyed it. Please consider leaving a review of this book at the place you bought it from, or contacting us with feedback, stuart@equiculture.com.au so that others may benefit from your reading experience.

17564876R00043

Printed in Great Britain
by Amazon